Christmas Treasures

11 Christmas Piano Solos
With Piano Duets

Arrangements by
GAIL LEW &
CHRIS LOBDELL

CONTENTS

Music Editor: GAIL LEW
Background Orchestrations: CHRIS LOBDELL
Cover Design: JOE KLUCAR
Book Art Layout: MICHAEL RAMSAY
Production Coordinator: KARL BORK

GAIL LEW

Gail Lew is the director of keyboard publications for Warner Bros. Publications in Miami, Florida. Gail has served as senior piano editor for Kjos Music in San Diego, new music reviewer for *California Music Teacher* magazine, and clinician for Frederick Harris Music Company in Toronto. She received her bachelor of music degree in piano performance and continued her graduate studies in music history and literature. Following graduate school, Gail pursued a career as a private piano instructor. She conducts yearly workshops in the United States and Canada, including presentations at the Music Teachers National Association Convention, many of its state affiliates, and the World Piano Pedagogy Conference.

Gail maintains an independent piano studio in Florida and serves in the children's ministry at her church. Gail has received national acclaim for her carefully edited and researched editions of contemporary music, her technic books for the *Technic Is Fun* series, and her arrangements of popular music for the *Looney Tunes Piano Library,* an educational supplemental library of piano music written specifically to correlate with all piano methods.

CHRIS LOBDELL

Chris Lobdell has established himself as a successful composer, teacher, studio musician, arranger, pianist, and producer on both the East and West Coasts. With compositions ranging from solo piano to full orchestral works, Mr. Lobdell has been engaged to write and orchestrate for the Miss America Pageant, produce full production shows for various cruise lines, create film and video soundtracks for national television commercials, and orchestrate background MIDI tracks for Warner Bros. Music Group, among other projects.

He is currently under contract as a composer, arranger, and orchestrator for Warner Bros. Publications, with ten solo piano books in worldwide circulation. Most recently, Chris arranged the MIDI accompaniment disks for the *Looney Tunes Piano Library* and *Frances Clark Music Tree* series, working directly with Gail Lew, director of keyboard publications at Warner Bros. Publications, and Sam Holland, professor of piano at Southern Methodist University. Chris has also arranged and produced numerous CD projects of various styles for many artists and choral groups. He is extremely active with his own production companies—North Riverside Studios and Chris Lobdell Productions—where he produces MIDI orchestrations used by teachers throughout the world.

Santa Claus Is Comin' to Town

Words and Music by
HAVEN GILLESPIE and J. FRED COOTS
Arranged by GAIL LEW and CHRIS LOBDELL

Wait 4 measures when playing with accompaniment.

*Optional rhythm for the student part may be taught at the discretion of the teacher.

Accompaniment *(student plays one octave higher)*   *Student begins:*

4

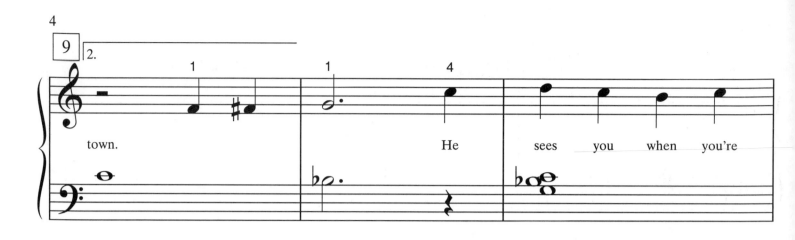

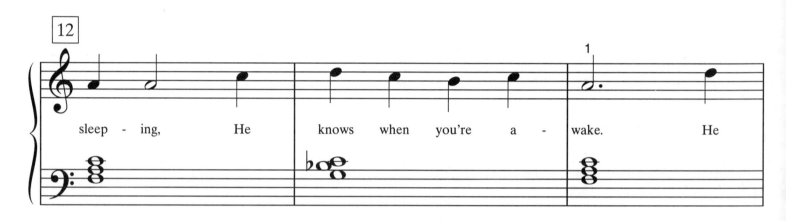

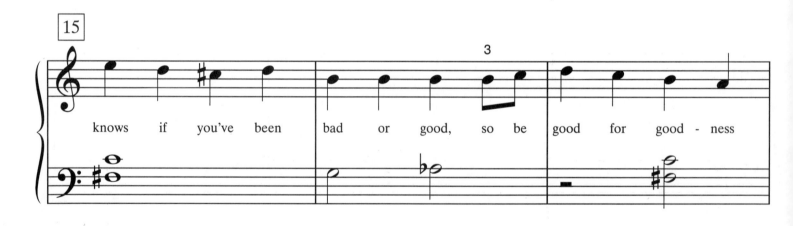

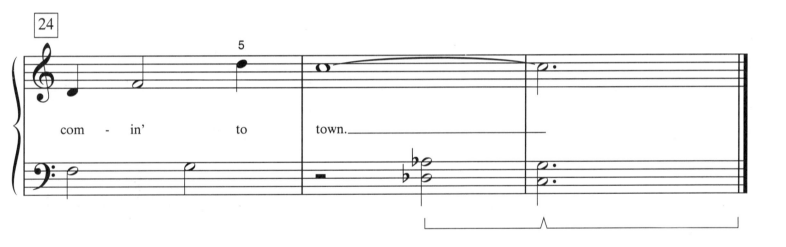

The First Noel

Track 2 · *Wait 4 measures when playing with accompaniment.*

TRADITIONAL
Arranged by GAIL LEW and CHRIS LOBDELL

Moderato

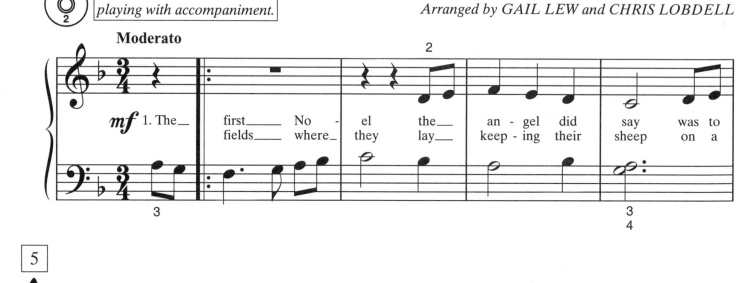

1. The first No - el the an - gel did say was to a
   fields where they lay keep - ing their sheep on a

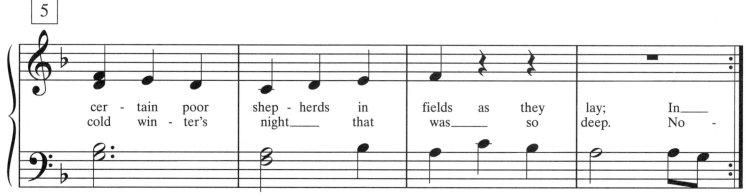

cer - tain poor shep - herds in fields as they lay; In No -
cold win - ter's night that was so deep.

Accompaniment *(student plays one octave higher)*　　　*Student begins:*

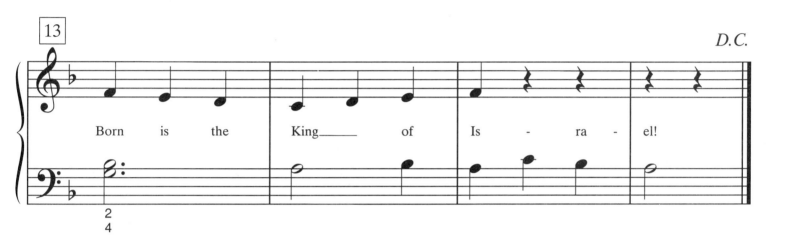

2. They looked up and saw a star,
   Shining in the East beyond them far;
   And to the earth it gave great light,
   And so it continued both day and night.
   Noel, Noel, Noel, Noel,
   Born is the King of Israel.

Silent Night

Track 3 — *Wait 4 measures when playing with accompaniment.*

Words and Music by
FRANZ GRUBER and JOSEPH MOHR
Arranged by GAIL LEW and CHRIS LOBDELL

(move 2 to B)

Accompaniment *(student plays one octave higher)*

Student begins:

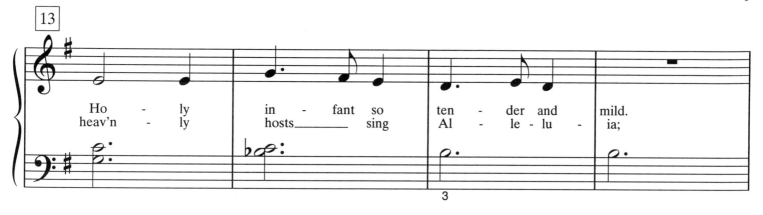

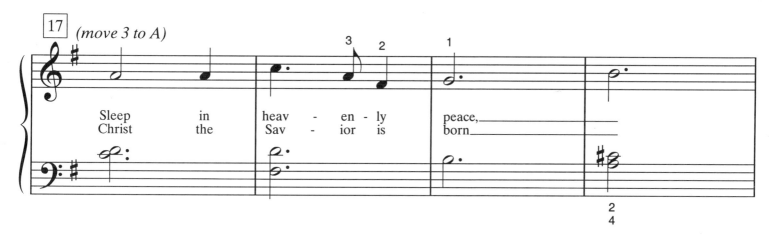

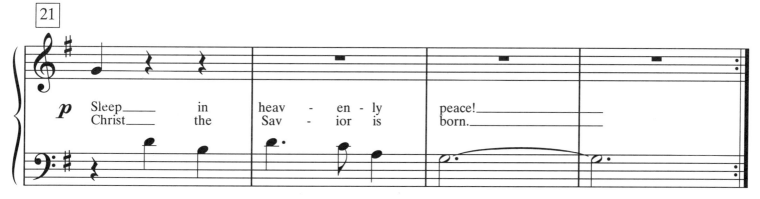

The Little Drummer Boy

Track 4 — *Wait 4 measures when playing with accompaniment.*

Words and Music by KATHERINE DAVIS,
HENRY ONORATI and HARRY SIMEONE
Arranged by GAIL LEW and CHRIS LOBDELL

ELM04017

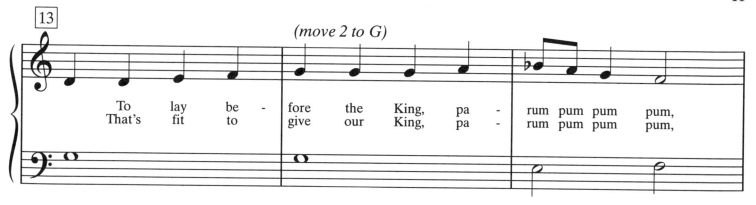

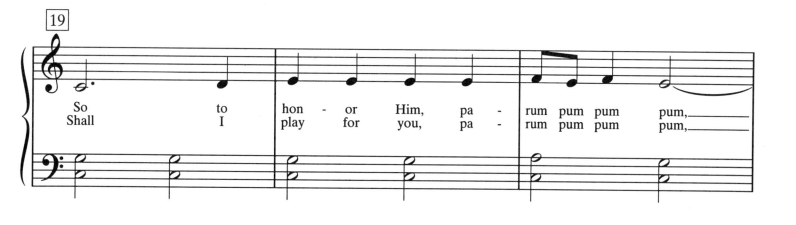

Hark! The Herald Angels Sing

Words by CHARLES WESLEY

Music by FELIX MENDELSSOHN
Arranged by GAIL LEW and CHRIS LOBDELL

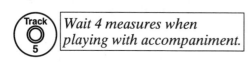

Wait 4 measures when playing with accompaniment.

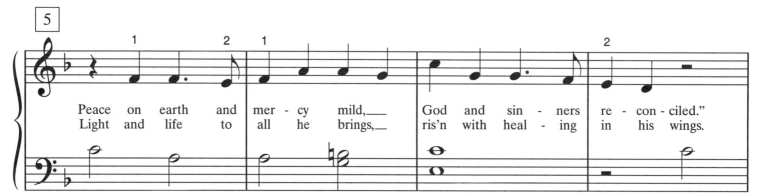

(move 2 to C)

Accompaniment *(student plays one octave higher)*

ELM04017

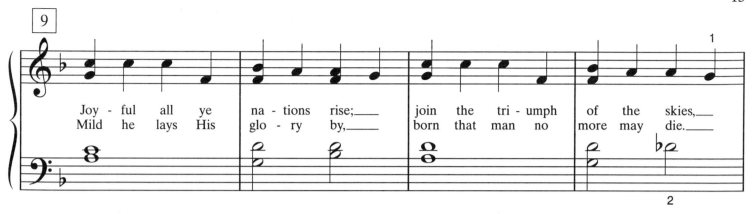

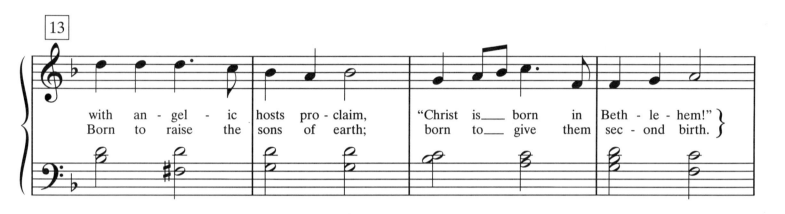

Angels We Have Heard on High

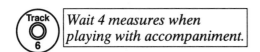
Wait 4 measures when playing with accompaniment.

TRADITIONAL
Arranged by GAIL LEW and CHRIS LOBDELL

Joyfully

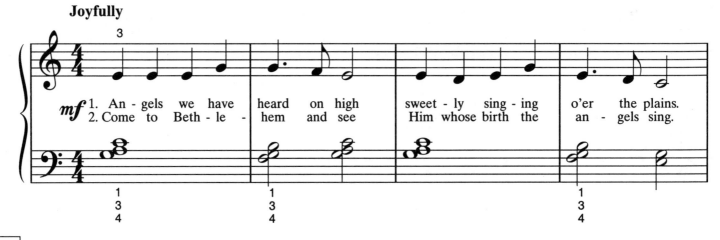

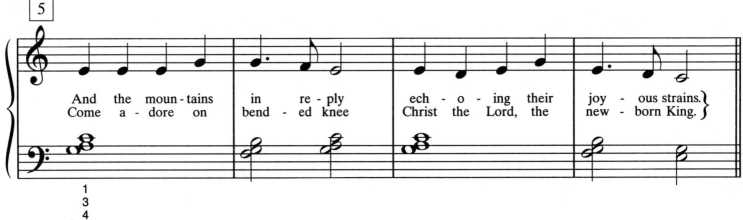

Accompaniment *(student plays one octave higher)*

Student begins:

ELM04017

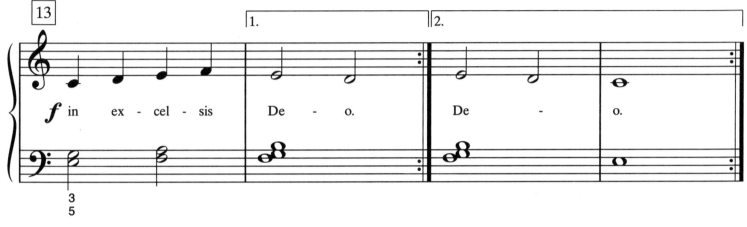

ELM04017

Go Tell It on the Mountain

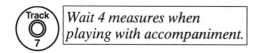

TRADITIONAL SPIRITUAL
Arranged by GAIL LEW and CHRIS LOBDELL

Moderato

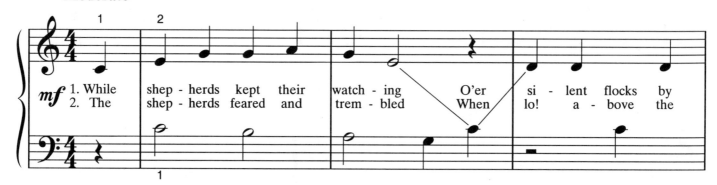

Accompaniment *(student plays one octave higher)*

ELM04017

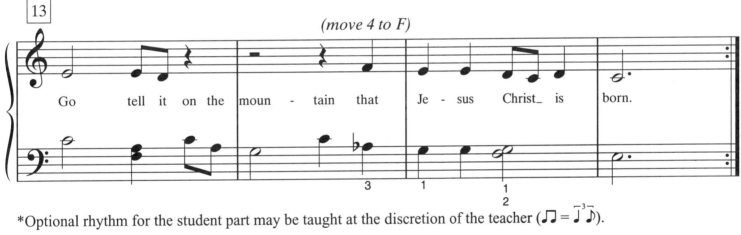

*Optional rhythm for the student part may be taught at the discretion of the teacher.

We Wish You a Merry Christmas

Wait 4 measures when playing with accompaniment.

TRADITIONAL ENGLISH CAROL
*Arranged by GAIL LEW
and CHRIS LOBDELL*

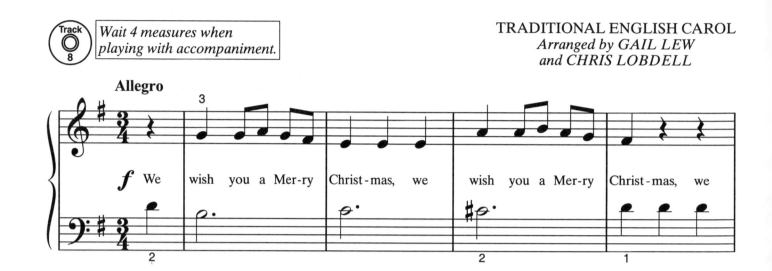

Accompaniment *(student plays one octave higher)*

Student begins:

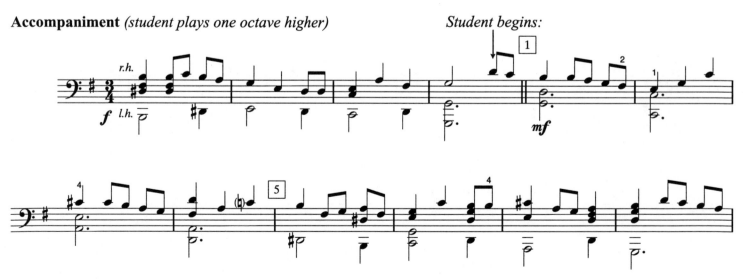

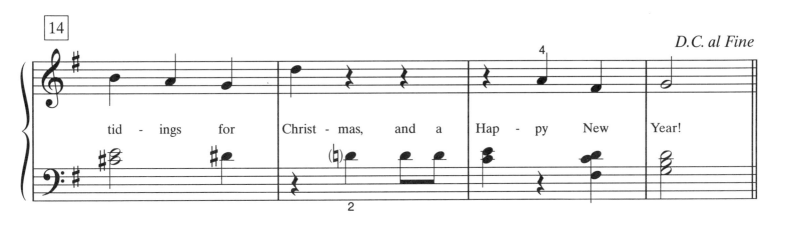

Frosty the Snowman

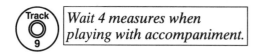

Wait 4 measures when playing with accompaniment.

Words and Music by
STEVE NELSON and JACK ROLLINS
Arranged by GAIL LEW and CHRIS LOBDELL

(move 3 to E)

Accompaniment (student plays one octave higher)

eyes made out of coal. came to life one day. There

must have been some mag - ic in that old silk hat they

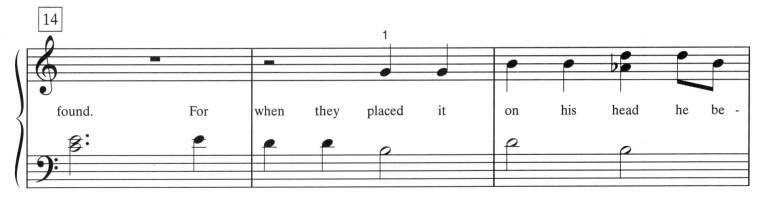

found. For when they placed it on his head he be -

gan to dance a - round. Oh, Frost - y the Snow - man was a -

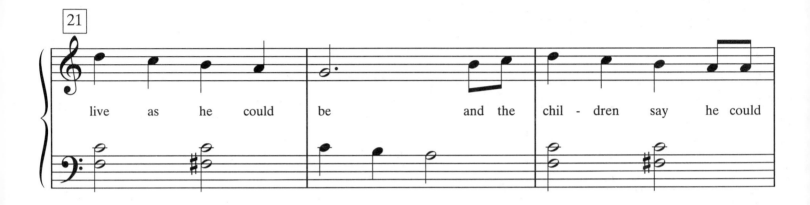

live as he could be and the chil - dren say he could

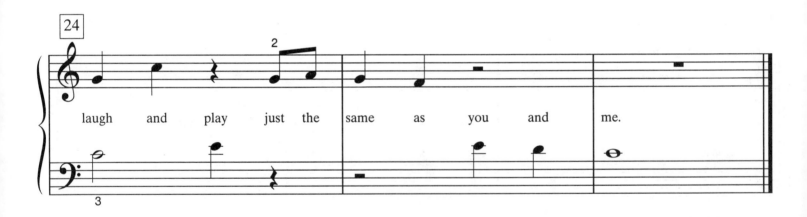

laugh and play just the same as you and me.

ELM04017

Jingle Bell Rock

Wait 4 measures when playing with accompaniment.

Words and Music by
JOE BEAL and JIM BOOTHE
Arranged by GAIL LEW and CHRIS LOBDELL

*Optional rhythm for the student part may be taught at the discretion of the teacher.

Accompaniment *(student plays one octave higher)*

Student begins:

ELM04017

24

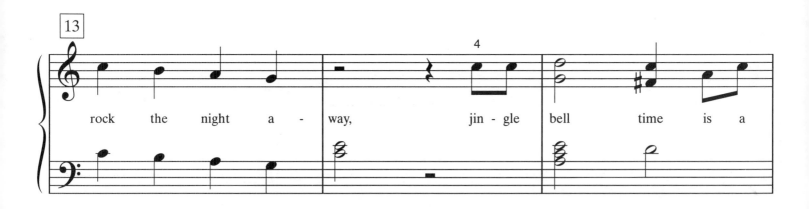

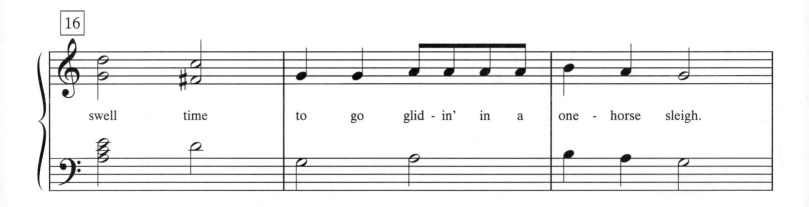

ELM04017

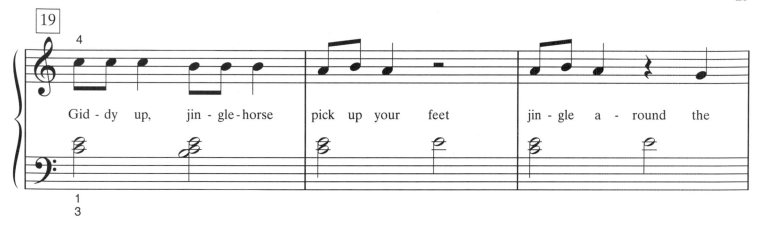

ELM04017

Jingle Bells

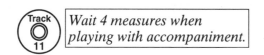

Words and Music by JAMES PIERPONT
Arranged by GAIL LEW and CHRIS LOBDELL

Wait 4 measures when playing with accompaniment.

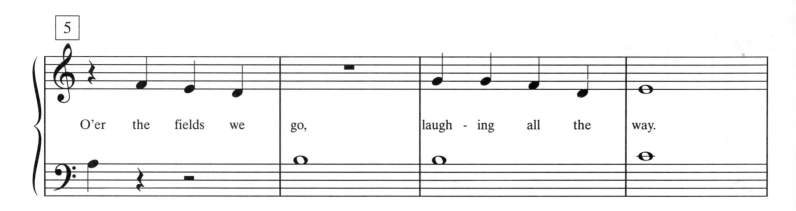

Accompaniment *(student plays one octave higher)*

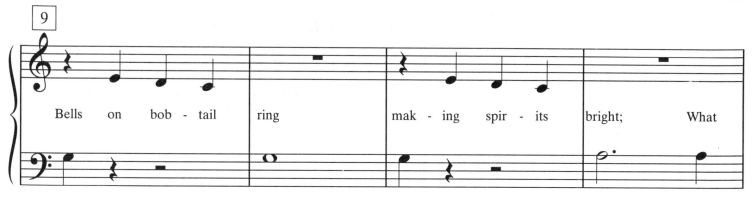

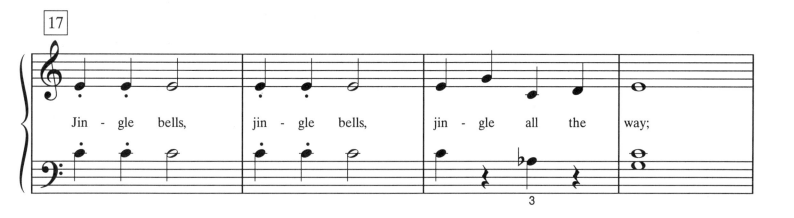

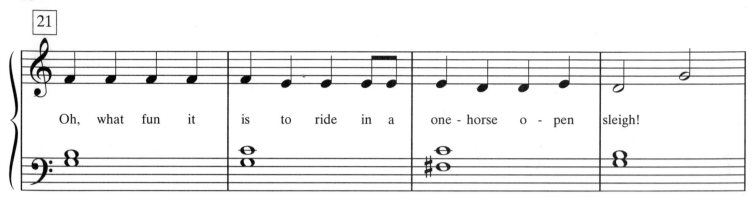

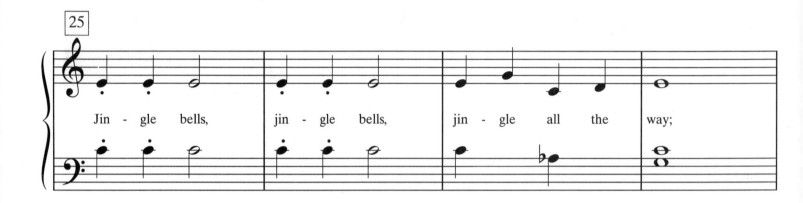

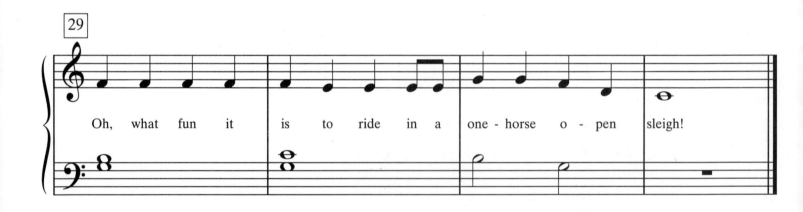

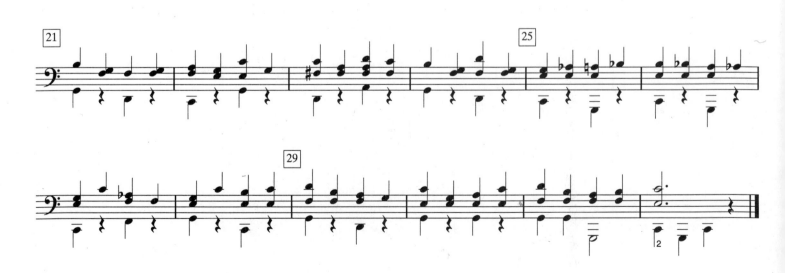

Piano Accompaniment

Level 2-3

Selections from

A STEVEN SPIELBERG FILM

INDIANA J

and the

KINGDOM OF
THE CRYSTAL SKULL ™

PARAMOUNT PICTURES PRESENTS A LUCASFILM LTD. PRODUCTION A STEVEN SPIELBERG FILM HARRISON FORD "INDIANA JONES AND THE KINGDOM OF THE CRYSTAL SKULL" CATE BLANCHETT KAREN ALLEN RAY WINSTONE JOHN HURT JIM BROADBENT AND SHIA LaBEOUF CASTING BY DEBRA ZANE C.S.A. VISUAL EFFECTS & ANIMATION BY INDUSTRIAL LIGHT & MAGIC MUSIC BY JOHN WILLIAMS EDITED BY MICHAEL KAHN A.C.E. COSTUME DESIGNER MARY ZOPHRES CO-PRODUCER DENIS L. STEWART DIRECTOR OF PHOTOGRAPHY JANUSZ KAMINSKI EXECUTIVE PRODUCERS GEORGE LUCAS KATHLEEN KENNEDY PRODUCED BY FRANK MARSHALL STORY BY GEORGE LUCAS AND JEFF NATHANSON SCREENPLAY BY DAVID KOEPP

IndianaJones.com

Alfred Publishing Co., Inc.
16320 Roscoe Blvd., Suite 100
P.O. Box 10003
Van Nuys, CA 91410-0003
alfred.com

Arranged by Bill Galliford, Ethan Neuburg and Tod Edmondson

ISBN-10: 0-7390-5668-9
ISBN-13: 978-0-7390-5668-4

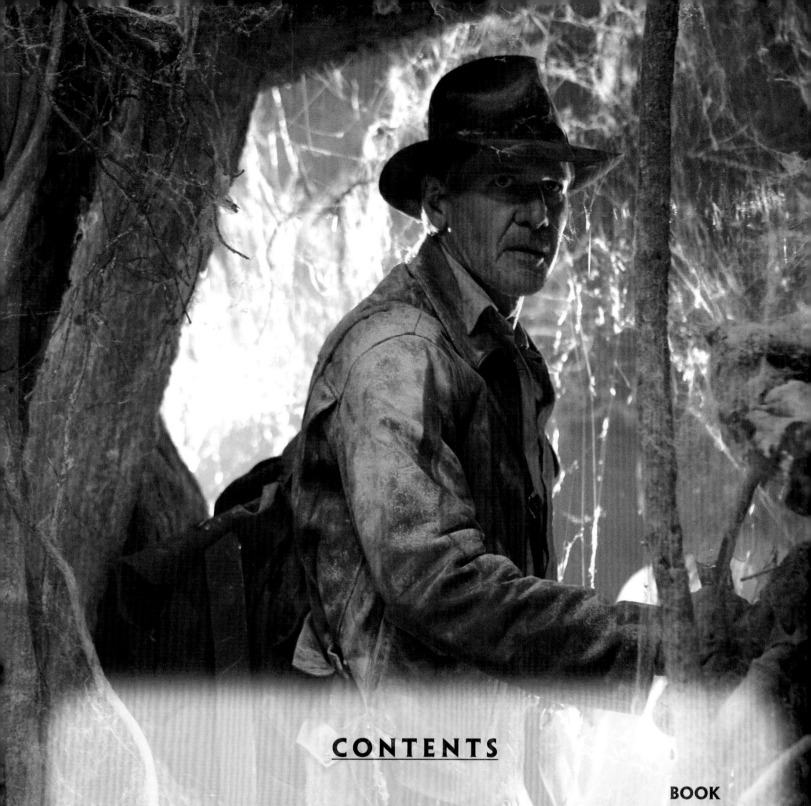

CONTENTS

MARION'S THEME
(as featured in RAIDERS MARCH)

Music by
JOHN WILLIAMS

Moderately slow, flowing (♩ = 104)

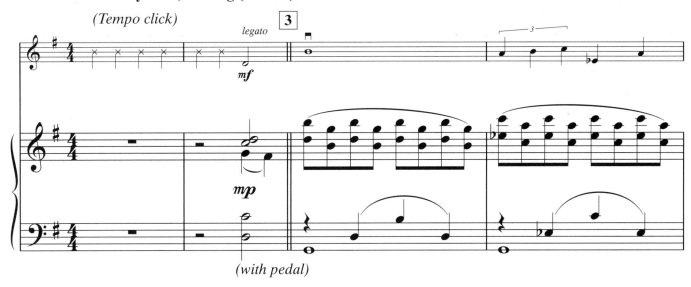

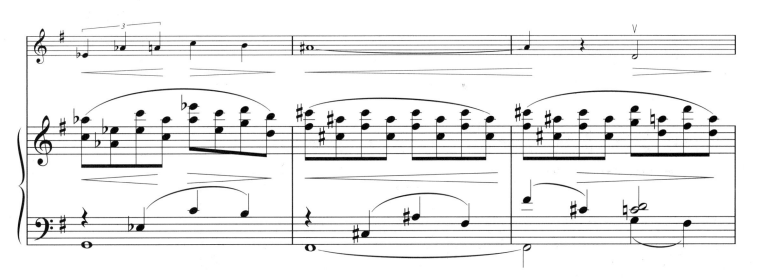

Marion's Theme - 3 - 1
31782

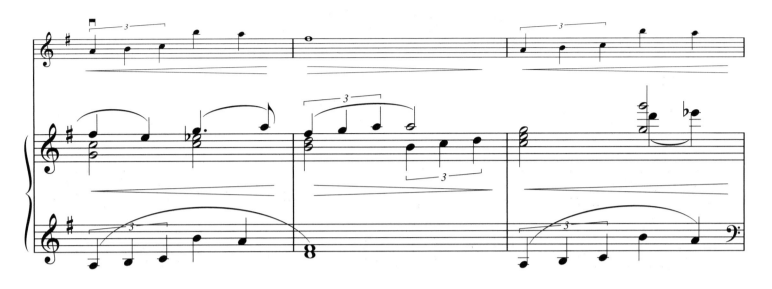

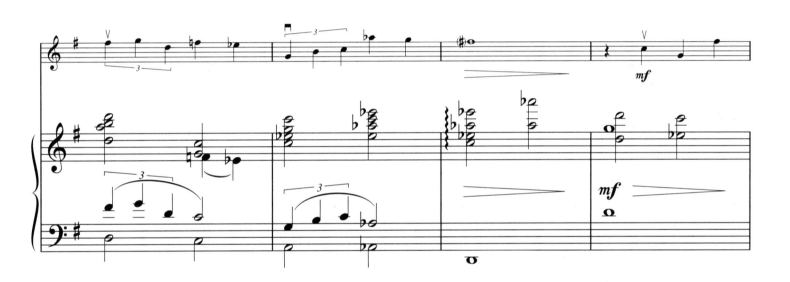

Marion's Theme - 3 - 3
31782

RAIDERS MARCH

Music by
JOHN WILLIAMS

Raiders March - 4 - 1
31782

10

Raiders March - 4 - 4
31782

THE ADVENTURES OF MUTT

Music by
JOHN WILLIAMS

Moderately bright (♩ = 132)

The Adventures of Mutt - 6 - 1
31782

14

The Adventures of Mutt - 6 - 6
31782

IRINA'S THEME

Moderato, espressivo (♩ = 72)

Music by
JOHN WILLIAMS

Irina's Theme - 2 - 1
31782

THE JOURNEY TO AKATOR

Music by
JOHN WILLIAMS

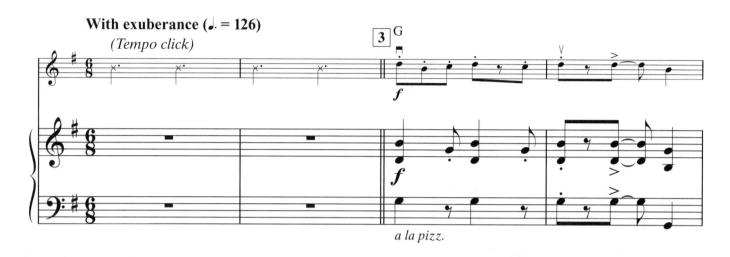

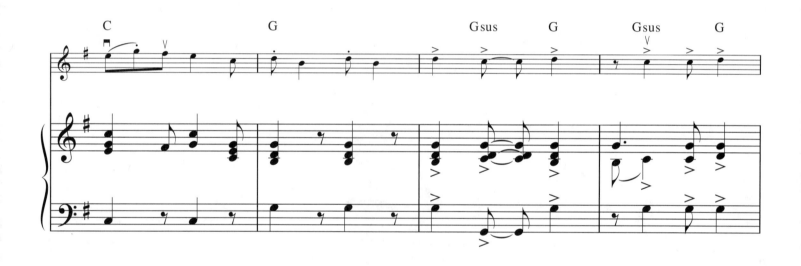

The Journey to Akator - 4 - 1
31782